MW00605646

FREE HUGS

By

Tiffany M. Cebrun

FREE HUGS

Copyright © 2020 by Tiffany M. Cebrun
All rights reserved. This book or any portion thereof may not be reproduced or used in any manner whatsoever without the express written permission of the publisher except for the use of brief quotations in a book review.

Printed in the United States of America

First Printing: 2020

ISBN: 978-1-952674-03-7

Publisher: LeRoyMac Publishing House

PUBLISHING HOUSE

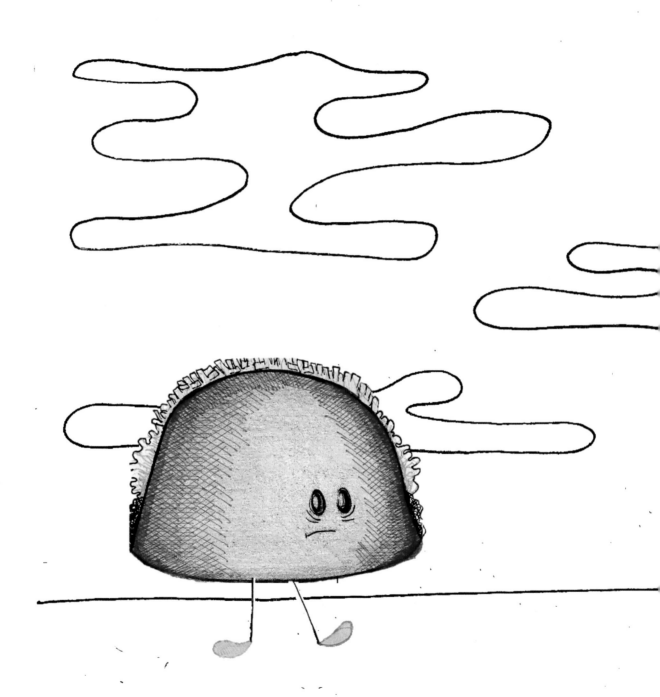

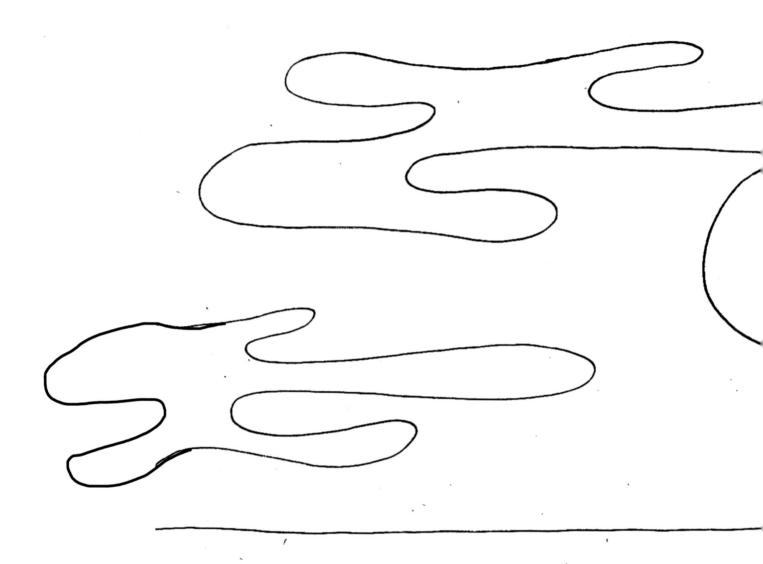

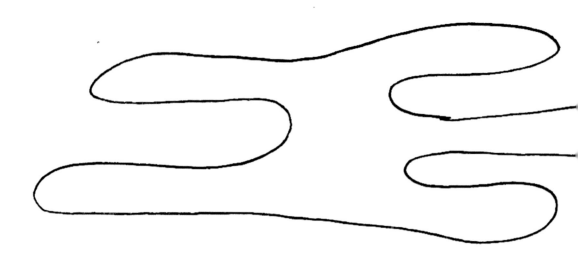

Made in the USA
San Bernardino, CA
28 June 2020

74517198R00022